Getty-Dubay
ITALIC HANDWRITING SERIES

Book D
Basic & Cursive Italic

Fourth Edition

by
Barbara Getty & Inga Dubay

Getty-Dubay Productions
Portland, Oregon USA

GETTY-DUBAY ITALIC HANDWRITING SERIES

BOOK A ▪ Basic Italic
14 mm body height

BOOK B ▪ Basic Italic
11 mm, 9 mm

BOOK C ▪ Basic Italic
9 mm, 6 mm   Introduction to Cursive Italic

BOOK D ▪ Cursive Italic
6 mm, 5 mm   including Basic Italic

BOOK E ▪ Cursive Italic
6 mm, 5 mm, 4 mm   including Basic Italic

BOOK F ▪ Cursive Italic
6 mm, 5 mm, 4 mm   including Basic Italic

BOOK G ▪ Cursive Italic
5 mm, 4 mm   including Basic Italic

INSTRUCTION MANUAL

FOURTH EDITION
Copyright 2010 by Barbara M. Getty and Inga S. Dubay
ISBN 978-0-9649215-7-3
THIRD EDITION
Copyright 1994 by Barbara M. Getty and Inga S. Dubay
SECOND EDITION
Copyright 1986 by Barbara M. Getty and Inga S. Dubay
REVISED EDITION
Copyright 1980 by Barbara M. Getty and Inga S. Dubay
FIRST EDITION
Copyright 1979 by Barbara M. Getty and Inga S. Dubay

14 13 12 11 10
10 9 8 7 6 5 4 3 2 1

Published by Getty-Dubay Productions
Portland, Oregon USA

Distributed by Allport Editions
2337 NW York
Portland, OR 97210 USA
www.allport.com

Printed with vegetable-based, no-VOC inks
on papers containing sustainable-harvest wood fibers and a minimum 30% post-consumer waste.

Printed in the United States of America.
Cover Design: Sinda Markham
Front cover picture: Waves hit the beach on the Oregon coast
Back cover pictures: Lighthouse at Bandon, Oregon; Avocets

CONTENTS

INTRODUCTION TO GETTY-DUBAY ITALIC HANDWRITING

This is the fourth of seven books in the Getty-Dubay Italic Handwriting Series and is recommended for third grade or advanced second grade. This book is designed to present the cursive joins in sequence, after a thorough review of basic italic. After all the joins are learned, then the cursive capitals are shown. (A student may prefer to continue using basic capitals with lowercase cursive.)

Writing practice includes first names, vowel sounds, consonant sounds, phonograms, prefixes, suffixes, homophones, homographs, ampersand, and punctuation. Sentence content includes poem forms such as couplet, haiku, acrostic, cinquain, limerick, formula poem, and tongue twisters. Cursive capital practice includes origins of our alphabet. Application form, letter writing and envelope making are presented, see INSTRUCTION MANUAL for lines and template.

TEACHER/STUDENT INSTRUCTIONS: Writing process/stroke information, directions, notes, reminders, options, and assessments are included in the margins. Further letter and join descriptions and assessment questions are found in the INSTRUCTION MANUAL.

ASSESSMENT: Assessment is the key to improvement. The self-assessment method used enables the student to monitor progress. STEP 1: the student is asked to LOOK at the writing and affirm what is the best. Questions are asked requiring a yes/no answer. 'Yes' is affirmation of a task accomplished. 'No' indicates work to be done. STEP 2: the student is asked to PLAN what needs to be improved and how to accomplish this. STEP 3: the student is asked to put the plan into PRACTICE. This *LOOK, PLAN, PRACTICE* format provides self-assessment skills applicable to all learning situations. Letter shape is the first focus. The next focus is on size, then spacing, and finally slope. Eventually the student has a checklist: letter shape, letter size, letter spacing, and letter slope. Use the *Slope Guidelines* to enable the student to find a personal slope choice. Speed is encouraged after letterforms and joins are learned. *Timed Writing* enables a gradual increase in the number of words written per minute while maintaining comfort and legibility. *Reading Looped Cursive* provides experience reading another writing style, while comparing legibility with italic handwriting.

CLASSROOM MANAGEMENT: Using direct instruction, present two pages a week, with follow-up practice on lined paper. Demonstrate the process/stroke sequence for letters and joins. This instruction, together with opportunities for integrating handwriting into other areas of curriculum, can provide 20 to 30 minutes of practice, 3 to 4 times a week. From day one, have DESK STRIPS and WALL CHART in place. For extra practice use BLACKLINE MASTERS. Have lined paper available that matches the 6mm, and 5mm lines used in this book (see *Reminders*). Lines at the back of this book and in the INSTRUCTION MANUAL may be duplicated. Write on the lines provided in this book or use thin paper for tracing over models in the book. Provide the opportunity for each student to select a page of his/her best handwriting to include in the student's portfolio.

This Fourth Edition includes join options and lift options for students to consider.

As a teacher, your interest and enthusiasm are instrumental in attaining the goal of legible and neat handwriting. The enjoyment of good handwriting is shared by both the writer and the reader. Handwriting is a lifelong skill. Good handwriting is a lifelong joy!

N.B. The information source for the writing practice is *The New Reading Teacher's Book of Lists* by Edward Fry et al. Source for origins of the alphabet is *Ancient Writing and Its Influence* by Berthold Ullman.

GETTY-DUBAY ITALIC HANDWRITING SERIES
BASIC & CURSIVE ITALIC ALPHABET

BASIC ITALIC

All letters written in one stroke unless otherwise indicated.   All letters start at the top except lowercase **d** and **e**.

CURSIVE ITALIC

All letters written in one stroke unless otherwise indicated.

GETTY-DUBAY ITALIC HANDWRITING REMINDERS

PENCIL HOLD

Use a soft lead pencil (#1 or #2) with an eraser. Hold the pencil with the thumb and index finger, resting on the middle finger. The upper part of the pencil rests near the large knuckle.

REGULAR HOLD

Hold the pencil firmly and lightly. AVOID pinching. To relax your hand, tap the index finger on the pencil three times.

Problem grips such as the 'thumb wrap' (thumb doesn't touch pencil) and the 'death grip' (very tight pencil hold) make it difficult to use the hand's small muscles. To relieve these problems, try this alternative pencil hold.

ALTERNATIVE HOLD

Place the pencil between the index finger and the middle finger. The pencil rests between the index and middle fingers by the large knuckles. Hold the pencil in the regular way at the tips of the fingers.

PAPER POSITION

LEFT-HANDED

If you are left-handed and write with the wrist below the line of writing, turn the paper clockwise so it is slanted to the right as illustrated. If you are left-handed and write with a "hook" with the wrist above the line of writing, turn the paper counter-clockwise so it is slanted to the left as illustrated. (Similar to the right-handed position.)

RIGHT-HANDED

If you are right-handed turn the paper counter-clockwise so it is slanted to the left as illustrated.

POSTURE

Rest your feet flat on the floor and keep your back comfortably straight without slumping. Rest your forearms on the desk. Hold the workbook or paper with your non-writing hand so that the writing area is centered in front of you.

LINED PAPER CHOICES:

The following choices for lined paper may be used when instructions say use lined paper for practice.

1. Lines 6mm body height on page 78 may be duplicated. These lines can also be used as guidelines under a sheet of unlined paper. Fasten with paper clips.

2. Lines 5mm body height on pages 79 & 80 may be duplicated. These lines can also be used as a line guide under a sheet of unlined paper. Lines on p. 80 also have a dotted line at capital height. Fasten with paper clips.

3. Some school paper has a solid baseline and a dotted waistline. Use paper with a body height of 6mm ($^1/_4$") or 5mm ($^3/_{16}$").

4. Some school paper has only baselines. Use paper with lines 12mm ($^1/_2$") or 10mm ($^3/_8$") apart.

5. Use wide-ruled notebook paper with a space of about 9 mm ($^3/_8$") between lines. Create your own waistline by lining up two sheets of notebook paper and shifting one down half a space. The faint line showing through will serve as a waistline. Fasten with paper clips.

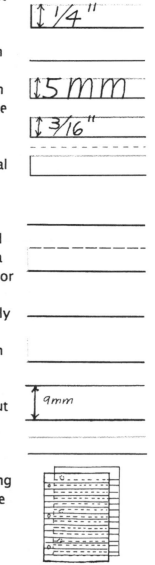

VOCABULARY

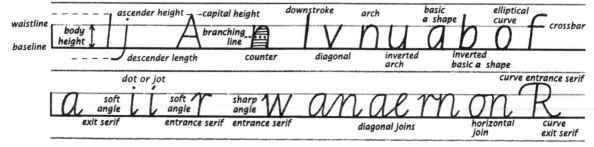

STROKES

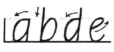

Basic italic letters all start at the top and go down or over (horizontal), except **d** and **e**, (**d** starts at the waistline and **e** starts at the center of the body height).
Follow the direction of the arrow. Letters are written in one stroke unless otherwise indicated. Trace the dotted line model, then copy model in space provided. If needed, trace solid line model.

LETTER DIMENSIONS

SHAPE

Basic italic lowercase letters are divided into eight families according to shape. Basic italic capitals are divided into three width groups. Cursive italic lowercase joins are divided into eight join groups.

SIZE

Letters are written with a consistent body height. Capitals, ascenders and descenders are written one and a half times the body height.

SLOPE

The models are written with a 5° letter slope. A consistent slope is an important part of good handwriting. For individual slope choices see *Slope Guidelines*, page 77.

SPACING

Letters are written close together within words. Joins are natural spacers in cursive italic; when lifts occur, keep letters close together. Spacing between words is the width of an **m** in basic italic and the width of an **n** in cursive italic.

SPEED

Write at a comfortable rate of speed. Though speed is not a primary concern at this level, students may use the *Timed Writing*, page 77.

GOAL

To write legible, neat handwriting.

IMPROVEMENT

Assessment is the key to improving your handwriting. Follow this improvement method as you learn basic and cursive italic handwriting.

- [1] **LOOK** at your writing. Circle your best letter or join. Answer question about strokes, shape, size, spacing, or slope.

- [2] **PLAN** how to make your writing look more like the model. Pick the letter or join that needs work. Compare with the model.

- [3] **PRACTICE** the letter or join that needs work. Write on the lines provided and on lined paper.

- Give yourself a star at the top of the page when you see you have made an improvement.

NOTE: See INSTRUCTION MANUAL, Assessment, pp. 54-68.

INFORMAL ASSESSMENT OF STUDENT PROGRESS

The main purpose of handwriting instruction is to promote legibility so that we can communicate with others and ourselves.

PRE-TEST Before beginning BOOK D, write the following sentence and today's date.

A quick brown fox jumps over the lazy dog.

Write the sentence.

today's date

Name

POST-TEST After you have completed BOOK D, write the following sentence and today's date in cursive italic.

A quick brown fox jumps over the lazy dog.

Write the sentence.

today's date

Name

ASSESSMENT

SHAPE:	Each letter is similar to the models in the workbook.
SIZE:	Similar letters are the same height (for example: aec, dhk, gpy). Capital letters and lowercase letters with ascenders are the same height.
SLOPE:	Letters have a consistent letter slope (between 5° – 15°).
SPACING:	Letters within words are closely spaced. Spaces between words are the width of **n**.
SPEED:	Words are written fluently at a comfortable speed.

PART I

GETTY-DUBAY BASIC ITALIC

LOWERCASE: 8 families

Family 1. straight line downstroke - i j l
Family 2. diagonal line - k v w x z
Family 3. arch - n h m r
Family 4. inverted arch - u y
Family 5. basic *a* shape - a d g q
Family 6. inverted basic *a* shape - b p
Family 7. elliptical curve - o e c s
Family 8. crossbar - f t

Improvement: shape, size

CAPITALS: 3 width groups

1. wide width - C G O Q D M W
2. medium width - T H A N K U V X Y Z
3. narrow width - E F L B P R S J I

Improvement: shape, size

LOWERCASE AND CAPITALS

Rules of capitalization and spacing practice

Improvement: spacing, size, slope

abcdefghijklmnopqrstuvwxyz

GETTY-DUBAY BASIC ITALIC LOWERCASE

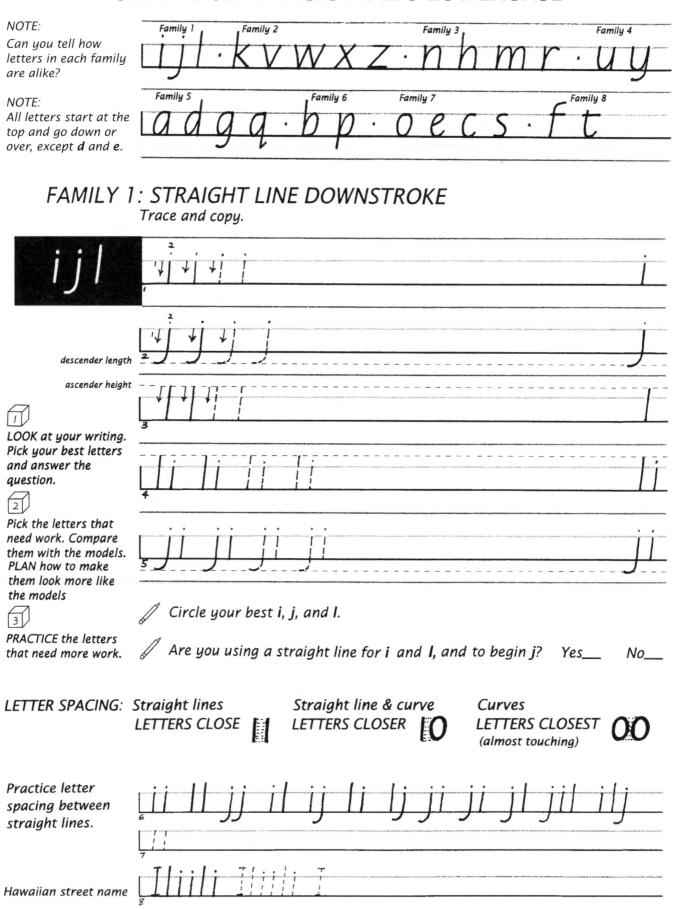

NOTE:
Can you tell how letters in each family are alike?

Family 1 Family 2 Family 3 Family 4
ijl · kvwxz · nhmr · uy

NOTE:
All letters start at the top and go down or over, except **d** and **e**.

Family 5 Family 6 Family 7 Family 8
adgq · bp · oecs · ft

FAMILY 1: STRAIGHT LINE DOWNSTROKE
Trace and copy.

i j l

descender length

ascender height

LOOK at your writing. Pick your best letters and answer the question.

Pick the letters that need work. Compare them with the models. PLAN how to make them look more like the models

PRACTICE the letters that need more work.

✏ Circle your best **i**, **j**, and **l**.

✏ Are you using a straight line for **i** and **l**, and to begin **j**?   Yes___   No___

LETTER SPACING: Straight lines
LETTERS CLOSE   Il

Straight line & curve
LETTERS CLOSER   Io

Curves
LETTERS CLOSEST   oo
(almost touching)

Practice letter spacing between straight lines.

ii ll jj il ij li lj ji ji jl jil ilj

Hawaiian street name   Iliili

FAMILY 2: DIAGONAL LINE
Trace and copy.

k v w x z   ascender height

k k k k   k

1. LOOK at your writing. Pick your best letters and answer the question.

v v v v   v

2. Pick the letters that need work. Compare them with the models. PLAN how to make them look more like the models.

w w w w   w

x x x x   x

3. PRACTICE those letters.

z z z z   z

ascender height

baseline   kiwi kiwi   kiwi

HINT:

K The corner of a sheet of paper fits here. This is a right angle.

✏ Circle your best **k**, **v**, **w**, **x**, and **z**.

✏ Are your letters sitting on the baseline?   Yes__   No__

LETTER SPACING: Straight line and diagonal line
(slightly closer than two straight lines)   **VI IV**

ki vi wi xi zi ik iv iw ix iz

NOTE:
The Hawaiian alphabet has twelve letters: *a, e, h, i, k, l, m, n, o, p, u,* and *w.*

will kiwi wikiwiki   Hawaiian word: fast, quick

PRACTICE here and on lined paper.

FAMILY 3: ARCH

Trace and copy.

n h m r   n n n n   n

ascender height

h h h h   h

NOTE: arch

branch out at
imaginary
branching line

m m m m   m

□1

LOOK at your writing.
Pick your best letters.
Answer the question.

r r r r   r

□2

PLAN how to make let-
ters more like models.

rim rim   rim

□3

PRACTICE here the
letters that need work.

hill hill   hill

✏ Circle your best **h**, **m**, **n**, and **r**.

✏ Are you making an arch shape?   Yes___   No___

PHONOGRAMS:
A phonogram is a
vowel sound plus a
consonant sound.
It is often less than
a syllable. It needs
an initial consonant
or blend to make it
a word.

-ill hill mill rill   -in kin win

-ill

-im him rim Kim Jim Tim

-im

-ink kink link rink wink

-ink

PRACTICE here and
on lined paper.

FAMILY 4: INVERTED ARCH (UPSIDE-DOWN ARCH)

Trace and copy.

u y

u u u u   u

NOTE:
upside down arch

branch in at
imaginary
branching line

y y y y   y

hum hum   hum

1. **LOOK** at your writing.

2. **PLAN** which letters need work. How will you make them look more like the models?

lily lily   lily

Circle your best **u** and **y**.

3. **PRACTICE** the letters that need more work.

Are you making an upside-down arch for **u** and **y**?   Yes___ No___

PHONOGRAMS:

-un nun run -um hum mum

-un

SUFFIX: -y

-unk hunk junk -y hilly

-unk

DOUBLE CONSONANTS:

mm mummy   nn runny

mm

ll willy-nilly w

PRACTICE here and on lined paper.

HINT:

n   Turn **n** upside down to see **u**.

FAMILY 5: BASIC *a* SHAPE
Trace and copy.

a d g q   a a a a   a

ascender height

NOTE:
branch in at imaginary branching line

a shape

descender length

a a a a   d

g g g g   g

NOTE:
Close up the top of *a, d, g,* and *q* so that *a* doesn't look like *u,*

a u

so that *d* doesn't look like *cl,*

d d

and so that *g* & *q* don't look like *y.*

g y q y

a a a a   q

and and   and

aqua aqua   aqua

✎ Circle your best *a, d, g,* and *q.*

✎ Are you making a basic *a* shape for *a, d, g,* and *q.*   Yes___ No___

PHONOGRAMS:

-ad glad had -ain drain rain

-ad

-ail quail mail -all hall wall

-ail

HINT:
flat head

soft angle (chin) curve

-ark dark mark -aw gnaw jaw

-ark

-awn dawn yawn -id did grid

-awn

More phonograms:
-ank, - ar, -ax, -ay, -ig, -ing, -ug

FAMILY 6: INVERTED BASIC **a** SHAPE (UPSIDE-DOWN BASIC **a** SHAPE)

Trace and copy.

b p

↓b ↓b ↑b b   b

NOTE:

branch out at
imaginary
branching line

↓p ↓p ↓p p   p

upside-down a shape

blip blip   blip

ascender height

descender length

bump bump   bump

LOOK

PLAN

Circle your best **b** and **p**.

Are you making an upside-down basic **a** shape for **b** and **p**?   Yes___ No___

PRACTICE

PHONOGRAMS:

-aid braid paid -ail bail pail

-aid

-ain brain plain -ark bark park

HINTS:

-ain

Turn **d**
upside down
to see **p**.

d

-ay bay pay -ump bump pump

-ay

Turn **q**
upside down
to see **b**.

q

-ip dip lip nip pip quip zip

-ip

**PRACTICE here the
letters that need work.**

FAMILY 7: ELLIPTICAL CURVE

Trace and copy.

o e c s   ơ ơ ơ   O

NOTE:

e   center of
    body height

e e e e   e

c c c c   c

NOTE:
Close up the top of
o so that o doesn't
look like **u**.

s s s s   s

LOOK at your writing.

oceans oceans   oceans

PLAN which letters
need work. How will
you make them look
more like the models.

Circle your best **o**, **e**, **c**, and **s**.

Are you starting **o**, **c**, and **s** at the waistline?   Yes___ No___

Practice those letters.

Are you starting **e** at the branching line?   Yes___ No___

PHONOGRAMS:

-ace space -ade shade -are care

-ace

More phonograms:
-ame, -ane, -ave,
-ear, -eep, -ed, -end,
-ew, -ick, -id, -ide,
-ime, -ine, ive, -oke,
-one, -ong, -op, -ow

-eak speak -eed speed -ell spell

-eak

HINT:
Notice the **o** reads
the same
right side
up as it
does upside down.

-ice slice -ide side -ive dive

-ice

-ope slope -orn corn -ush slush

-ope

PRACTICE here and
on lined paper.

FAMILY 8: CROSSBAR

Trace and copy.

f t   f f f f   f

t   t t t t   t

NOTE: Ascender of t is shorter than the ascender of f.

fast fast   fast

The crossbar joins f and t.

lift lift   lift

✏ Circle your best f and t.

✏ Are your crossbars of f and t at the waistline?   Yes___ No___

PHONOGRAMS:

-act fact   -aft craft   -at that

-act

1. LOOK at your writing.

-ate fate   -eat neat   -eet feet

-ate

2. PLAN which letters need work.

-ent tent   -est test   -et jet

-ent

3. PRACTICE the letters that need more work.

-ight tight   -int tint   -it fit

-ight

HINT: f t

-iff stiff   -ift lift   -ot tot

-iff

End the crossbar of f so it lines up with the ascender.

End the crossbar of t so it lines up with the curve.

-uff stuff   -ut shut   ff ff   ft ft   tt

-uff

GETTY-DUBAY BASIC ITALIC CAPITALS:
WIDE, MEDIUM and NARROW

Trace and copy.

WIDE

width equals height

M and W slightly wider

capital height

✏ Are your C, G, O, Q, and D wide?   Yes___ No___

✏ Are your M and W slightly wider?   Yes___ No___

PRACTICE letters here and on lined paper.

NOTE:
All capitals start at the top.

MEDIUM

width is ⁴/₅ of height

✏ Are your letters medium width?   Yes___ No___

PRACTICE letters here and on lined paper.

HINT: To help remember the medium width letters they spell "Thank U (you) V, X, Y, and Z."

NARROW

width is ¹/₂ of height

E F L B P R S J I

E F L B P R S J I

NOTE:
All capitals start at the top.

🖊 Are your letters narrow width?   Yes___ No___

PRACTICE letters here and on lined paper.

NOTE:
For Basic Italic Capital assessment, see INSTRUCTION MANUAL.

REVIEW: GETTY-DUBAY CAPITALS AND LOWERCASE   *Trace and copy.*

capital and ascender height

Aa Bb Cc Dd Ee Ff Gg

descender length

Hh Ii Jj Kk Ll Mm Nn Oo

Pp Qq Rr Ss Tt Uu Vv W

W Xx Yy Zz

Copy the models and practice on lined paper.

GETTY-DUBAY BASIC ITALIC CAPITALS & LOWERCASE:
RULES OF CAPITALIZATION

capital and ascender height

1. Sentences begin with capitals.

All sentences begin with

a capital letter.

capital and ascender height

A

RULES OF SPACING LETTERS   *There are three widths of spacing letters in words.*

1. Wide space between straight line downstrokes.   *capital Ellen*

2. Medium space between straight line and curve.   *Bob Ellen*

3. Narrow space between two curves at the center. Narrow space between diagonal and downstroke at the waistline.   *Chloe David*

2. Names of people are capitalized.

Bob   Chloe   David   Ellen

B

Trace and complete.   *My name is*

Trace and copy line above.   *M*

Trace and copy.

3. Names of places are capitalized.

France   Geneva   Hawaii

F

Write the name of your city, state, and country.

I live in

4. Pronoun 'I' is capitalized.

I know I can write.

I

5. Names of months are capitalized.

June September October

J

Trace and complete.

This month is

LOOK at your writing. Choose one:

✎ Circle your best wide spacing between straight lines.

✎ Circle your best medium spacing between a straight line and a curve.

✎ Circle your best narrow spacing between two curves.

PLAN which letters need work.

PRACTICE those letters.

SIZE: *Capital and lowercase ascender height is halfway between waistline and top line.*

6. Days of the week are capitalized.

Sunday Monday Tuesday

Trace and copy. S

Wednesday Thursday Friday

W

Saturday S

Trace and complete. Today is

7. Book titles are capitalized and underlined.

The Wind in the Willows

T

8. Official titles are capitalized.

President
Trace and complete.

9. Capitalize 'uncle' and 'aunt' when used with a name.

Uncle Quincy Aunt Ruth

U

Are your ascenders the same height as your capitals? Yes___ No___

PRACTICE letters here.

SLOPE: *Straight line downstrokes are parallel to 5° slope.*

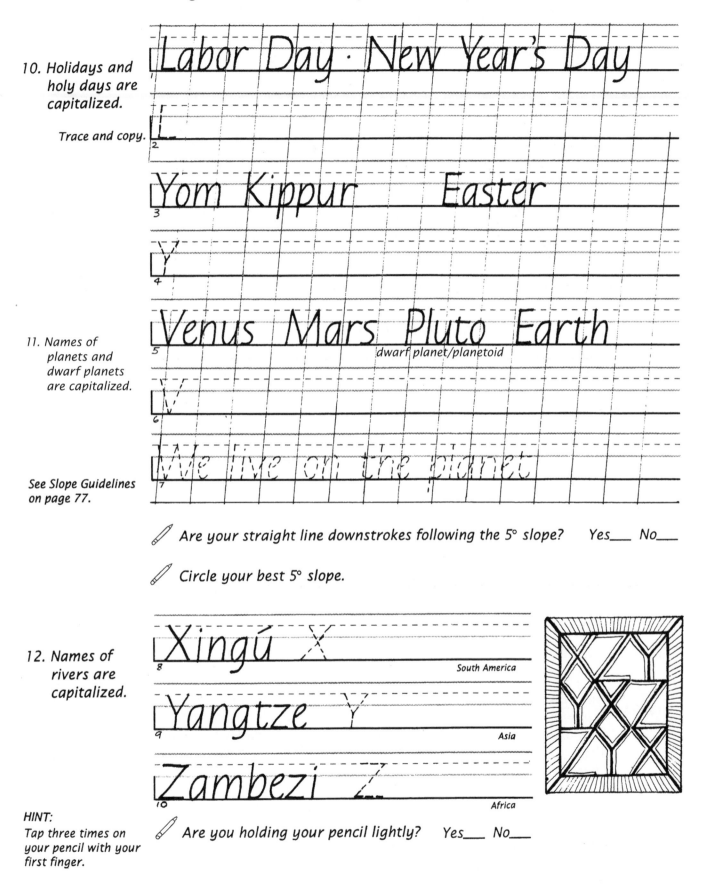

10. Holidays and holy days are capitalized.

Labor Day · New Year's Day

Trace and copy.

Yom Kippur   Easter

11. Names of planets and dwarf planets are capitalized.

Venus Mars Pluto Earth
                    dwarf planet/planetoid

We live on the planet

See Slope Guidelines on page 77.

✐ Are your straight line downstrokes following the 5° slope?   Yes___ No___

✐ Circle your best 5° slope.

12. Names of rivers are capitalized.

Xingú   X
                    South America

Yangtze   Y
                    Asia

Zambezi   Z
                    Africa

HINT:
Tap three times on your pencil with your first finger.

✐ Are you holding your pencil lightly?   Yes___ No___

USES OF GETTY-DUBAY BASIC ITALIC

Basic italic, sometimes called "printing," is useful for many purposes, such as posters, maps, announcements, and for filling out applications and forms.

For a poster, write the most important words in capital letters. Notice that the letters all sit on an imaginary baseline.

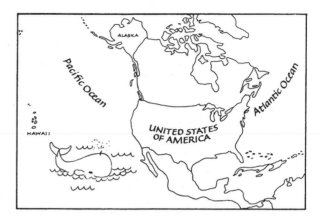

Maps are always written with unjoined letters. The names of large areas, such as countries and states, are written in capital letters.

BOOK SALE
Library
Today at 3:15

When a form says "Prease print," use basic italic.

APPLICATION FORM Please print

Name: _____
　　　　　　　　Last　　　　　　　First　　　　　　　Middle

Address: _____
　　　　　　　　Street

　　　　　_____
　　　　　　　City　　　　　　　　　State　　　Zip Code

School: _____ Age: _____

GIVE YOUR WRITING A STAR

Look at the pages of writing you have just completed. Pick one page that shows the most improvement. Give yourself a star at the top of that page! Good for you! If it was a big improvement, give yourself two stars. Show the starred page to a friend and tell how you improved your handwriting. Do the letter shapes look more like the models? Is your letter size more even? Is your letter slope more even? Is your letter spacing more even? GOOD WORK!

NEXT STEP: From Basic Italic to Cursive Italic

After you have learned the basic letter shapes, you are ready for the next step. On the following pages you will begin to join letters. This is called cursive writing. It is the kind of writing you will use everyday.

PART 2
GETTY-DUBAY CURSIVE ITALIC

TRANSITION TO CURSIVE ITALIC

Addition: descender for f
Options: dot or jot for i and j, two-stroke k or one-stroke k
Serifs: soft angle exit serifs - a d h i k l u n m z
  soft angle entrance serifs - r n m x z
  sharp angle entrance serifs - j p v w

Improvement: shape

CURSIVE ITALIC LOWERCASE: 8 JOINS

Join 1. diagonal - *an*
Join 2. diagonal swing up - *au*
Join 3. diagonal start back - *ao*
Join 4. diagonal into e - *ae*
Join 5. horizontal - *on*
Join 6. diagonal out of r - *ru*
Join 7. horizontal to diagonal - *sn*
Join 8. diagonal to horizontal - *aa*
Lifts - lift before f and z; lift after g j q y
Pangrams

Improvement: shape, size, spacing, slope

NUMERALS

CURSIVE CAPITALS

Origins: Egyptian, Phoenician, Greek, Roman
Writing practice using first names

Improvement: shape, size, slope

Vowel sounds, consonant sounds, poem forms, phonograms, homophones,
homographs, prefixes, suffixes, letter and envelope writing

Improvement: shape, size, spacing, slope

READING LOOPED CURSIVE

Comparison of cursive italic handwriting with looped cursive handwriting

SLOPE, SPEED
Slope Guidelines
Timed Writing

abcdefghijklmnopqrstuvwxyz

ADDITION & OPTIONS:

ADDITION:	OPTION:	OPTION: k may also be a
f adds a descender	i and j use a dot or jot	one-stroke letter
f·f	i·i or í j·j or j	k·k or k

SERIFS: Serifs are lines added to letters.

There are exit serifs and entrance serifs.

Serifs are like hands reaching out to join letters.

EXIT SERIF: End with a soft angle at the baseline into a short diagonal. *(n, m, and x also have entrance serifs.)*

←diagonal

soft angle

AVOID a hook

AVOID a scoop

a·a a	d·d d
h·h h	i·i i
k·k k	l·l l
m·m m	n·n n
u·u u	x·x x

1 LOOK at your writing. Pick your best letters. Answer the question.

✎ Circle some of your best exit serifs.   Yes___ No___

✎ Are your letters ending with a soft angle exit serif?   Yes___ No___

2 Pick the letters that need work. Compare them with the models. PLAN how to make them look more like the models.

3 PRACTICE here the letters that need work.

ENTRANCE SERIFS:

There are two kinds of entrance serifs—soft angle entrance serifs and sharp angle entrance serifs.

SOFT ANGLE
ENTRANCE SERIF:

soft angle

diagonal →

m · m · m   n · n · n

r · r · r   x · x · x

✏ Circle your best soft angle entrance serif.

SHARP ANGLE
ENTRANCE SERIF: Begin with a short diagonal line to a sharp angle.

sharp angle

diagonal →

j · j · j   p · p · p

v · v · v   w · w · w

✏ Circle your best sharp angle entrance serif.

PRACTICE the letters
that need more work.

AVOID a scoop

CURSIVE Z: Add short entrance and exit serifs to z.

z · z · z

✏ Circle your best z.

REVIEW: CURSIVE ITALIC LOWERCASE LETTERS

a b c d e f g h i j k l m
or k

1 Trace and copy.
LOOK at your writing.

a

2 PLAN which letters
need work.

n o p q r s t u v w x y z

3 PRACTICE those letters
on lined paper.

n

JOIN 1: DIAGONAL

Join 1 is a straight diagonal line from the baseline to the waistline into n, m, r, and x.

a / an   **an**   an · an cn dn en

diagonal
to soft angle

Trace and copy. *an*

hn in kn ln mn nn un

nn

zn · Ann Ben Dan Jan

zn

A straight diagonal
line is the shortest
distance between
two serifs.

an   Ken MuLan Vin

K

✏ Circle one of your best diagonal joins.

a / am   **am**   am · am em im mm

diagonal
to soft angle

am

um · Jim Kim Lem

um

NOTE:
AVOID a wavy line
am

Pam Sam Tim

P

✏ Circle your best diagonal join into m.

ar aȓ

**diagonal
to soft angle**

ar

Trace and copy.

aȓ · ar cr dr er ir

ar

kr ur · Mar Mer

kr

A straight diagonal line is the shortest distance between two letters.

✏ Circle your best diagonal join into **r**.

ar aȓ

**diagonal
to soft angle**

ax

ax · ax ex ix ux

ax

Lex Max Tex

LOOK at your writing.
Pick your best join.

✏ Circle your best diagonal join into **x**.

REVIEW: JOIN 1   *Using a diagonal join write Dan, Pam, Mar, and Max.*

D

OPTION: Join into n, m, r, and x with Diagonal Swing Up (Join 2).

ar an

**diagonal
swing up**

an en in un · am em im um

an

ar er ir ur · ax ex ix ux

ar

Ann Ben Pam Tim Mer Max

A

JOIN 2: DIAGONAL SWING UP

Join 2 is a straight diagonal line from the baseline to the branching line, then swing up to the waistline or ascender height. Join into **b, h, i, j, k, l, p, t, u, v, w,** *and* **y.** *Optional join into* **n, m, r,** *and* **x.**

a → au
diagonal
swing up

au   *au   au   cu   du   eu   hu*

Trace and copy.   *au*

imaginary
branching line

iu   ku   lu   mu   nu   zu · Liu

iu

✏ Circle your best join into **u.**

a → ay
diagonal
swing up

ay   *ay · ay   cy   dy   ey   hy*

ay

iy   ky   ly   my   ny   uy   zy

uy

NOTE:
diagonal to branching line

soft angle
exit serif

Amy   Aly   Fay   Guy   Jay

A

Kay   Ray   Suzy

Letters join
at the
branching
line.

K

AVOID scoop

scoop

Benny   Danny   Jimmy

B

✏ Circle your best join into **y.**

a, ai
*diagonal
swing up*

ai | ai · ai ci di ei hi ii

Trace and copy.

ki li mi ni ui zi · Aki

Ali Cai Kimi Lei Mei

Mimi Rai Sumi Tami

Circle your best join into **i**.

a, aj
*diagonal
swing up*

aj | aj · aj ej ij iy

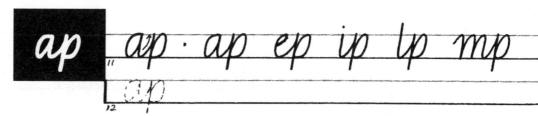

Circle your best join into **j**.

a, ap
*diagonal
swing up*

ap | ap · ap ep ip lp mp

Join into **p** at the
branching line. ····

up · Cap Kip

Circle your best join into **p**.

a→ at
diagonal
swing up

at

Trace and copy.

at · at · at · ct · et · it

at

REMINDER: **t** has a
short ascender.

tt · nt · ut · Kit Pat

tt

NOTE: DOUBLE T
long crossbar

tt

large **u** shape

tt · tt · tt · Matt

tt

🖊 *Does your **t** have a short ascender?* Yes___ No___

a→ al
diagonal
swing up

al

al · al · cl · el · il · ll · ul

al

Cal Emil Emily Felix Jill

REMINDER: Ascender
height and capital
height are the same.

Kalim Kelly Lily Mel Neil

K

al

Join into **l** at the
branching line.

Paul Phillip Sally

P

🖊 *Circle your best join into **l**.*

PRACTICE here the
joins that need work
and on lined paper.

aₐaʰh
**diagonal
swing up**

ah | *aʰh · ah ch eh ih uh*

Trace and copy.

ah

Elijah Ichi Mahir Nahum

E

✎ Circle your best join into **h.**

aₐaᵇb
**diagonal
swing up**

ab | *aᵇb · ab eb ib ub · Web*

ab

✎ Circle your best join into **b.**

aₐaᵏk
**diagonal
swing up**

ak | *aᵏk · ak ck ek ik*

ak

**Join at imaginary
branching line.**

kk lk nk uk · Aki Kiku

kk

AVOID scoop and loop

al

Malik Yuki Zak

M

✎ Circle your best join into **k.**

**PRACTICE here the
joins that need work.**

a, av
diagonal
swing up

av | av · av ev iv

Trace and copy.

av

Join into v with a
diagonal swing up to
the waistline.

uv · Bev Lev Liv

uv

✏ Circle your best join into **v**.

a, av
diagonal
swing up

aw | aw · aw ew iw uw · Lew

aw

✏ Circle your best join into **w**.

OPTION: You may use a soft angle at the bottom of **v** and **w**.

v w
↑ ↑↑
soft angle

Bev Lev Liv Lew

Bev

v w
↑ ↑↑
sharp angle

✏ Do you like a sharp angle or soft angle at the bottom
of v and w?   sharp___   soft___   don't know yet___

REVIEW: JOIN 2

Using Join 2 write Pat, Lew, Paul, Kelly, and Philip.

imaginary branching line··

1 LOOK at your writing.
Pick your best join.
Answer the question.

✏ Circle one of your best diagonal swing up joins.

✏ Are you joining at the imaginary branching line?   Yes___   No___

2 PLAN how to make
joins more like models.

3 PRACTICE here the
joins that need work.

OPTION: *Join into* **n**, **m**, **r**, *and* **x** *with Diagonal Swing Up.*

a, a'n

an cn dn en hn in kn ln

an

mn nn un zn · Ann Ben

mn

Dan Jan Ken MuLan Vin

D

REMINDER: *Tap your index finger on the pencil three times to help avoid pinching. See Pencil Hold on page vi.*

am em im mm um · Jim

am

Kim Lem Pam Sam Tim

K

ar cr dr er ir kr ur · Mar

ar

ax ex ix ux · Lex Max Tex

ax

Which join into **n**, **m**, **r**, *and* **x** *is easier for you to write?*

Diagonal Roll Over

an am ar ax ____

Diagonal Swing Up

an am ar ax ____

Using your choice of joins write Dan, Pam, Mar, & Max.

D

JOIN 3: DIAGONAL START BACK

Join 3 is a straight diagonal line from the baseline to the waistline then start back into o.

ao *ao*
diagonal
start back

ao

Trace and copy.

ao · ao co do eo ho io

ao

NOTE:
Close up the top of
o so that o doesn't
look like u.

ko lo mo no uo zo · Leo

ko

Emilio Julio Paulo

E

Keep the o an
elliptical shape.

✏ Circle one of your best diagonal joins into o.

REVIEW: JOIN 3 Write Leo, Emilio, Julio, and Paulo.

1 LOOK

2 PLAN

3 PRACTICE

✏ Are you joining into o and s with a straight diagonal line? Yes____ No____

OPTION: Join into s with a straight diagonal line.
Leave off the horizontal top of s.

as *as*
diagonal
start back

as cs ds es hs is ks ls ms

as

ns us · Gus Les Willis

ns

OPTION: Use Join 8 where the s shape is unchanged. (see page 43)

as *as*
diagonal
to horizontal

as cs ds es hs is ks ls ms ns us

as

JOIN 4: DIAGONAL INTO *e*

Join 4 is a straight diagonal line to the branching line into the center of **e**.

a, ae
diagonal
into e

ae · ae ce de ee he ie

Trace and copy.

ke le me ne ue ze

OPTION: For two-stroke
e see INSTRUCTION
MANUAL.

ene

Join into e at the
branching line.

Anne Alex Clem Eileen

accent

Gene Helen Inés Jaime

James Janet Kalle Lee

AVOID
scoop
and loop

ae

Melei Sue Umeko

☐1 LOOK at your writing.

☐2 PLAN how to make joins
more like the models.

☐3 PRACTICE

Circle your best diagonal join into e.

REVIEW: JOIN 4 Write Anne, Gene, Helen, and Janet.

OPTION: Lift before e.

NOTE:
When lifting between
letters, keep letters
close together.

ae ce de ee he ie ke le me ne ue ze

ae

JOIN 5: HORIZONTAL

Join 5 is a horizontal join at the waistline. Join out of o, t, f, v, w, and x into every letter except f.

σ⃗ on

horizontal

on   on · on om or ox · Don

Trace and copy.   *on*

Jon Leon Tom Tony Thor

J

NOTE:
AVOID scoop

ou

ou oy oi oj op ov ow · Joy

ou

Jojo Lois Louis Zhou   OU

J

Join with a
horizontal at
the waistline.

NOTE:
Close up the top of
o so that **o** doesn't
look like **u**.

oo oa oc od og oq os oz

oo

Hoa Joan Jock Noah

NOTE:
AVOID scoop

✏ Circle one of your best joins out of **o**.

σ⃗ ol ot

horizontal
swing up into
short ascender of **t**

ot ot Dot Lot

ot

OPTION: Lift before **t.**

NOTE:
Avoid
diagonal

o't   ot Dot Lot *ot*

Trace and copy.

ō ōl

horizontal swing up into ascender

ol oh ob ok · Bob

Join with a horizontal and swing up into the ascender.

NOTE: Avoid diagonal into **l**, **h**, **b**, and **k**.

ōl

John Polly Colleen Yoko

OPTION: Lift before ascenders after **o**.

ol oh ob ok Bob Polly Yoko

ol

OPTION: Join into **e** after **o**.

ō oe

*diagonal into **e** (counter of **e** is smaller*

oe Cloe Joe Joel Noel Zoe

oe

OPTION: Lift before **e** after **o**.

oe Cloe Joe Joel Noel Zoe

oe

NOTE: When lifting between letters, be sure to keep letters close together. Joins are natural spacers -- when not using a join, keep letters close.

1 LOOK at your writing. Pick your best join.

2 Pick the joins that need work. Compare them with the models.

3 PRACTICE here the joins that need work.

t⃗ tr
horizontal out of the crossbar

tr

Trace and copy.

tr tr tr · tu ty ti tw

ty

Katy Katie

ty
Join out of the crossbar.

tt tt tt

REMINDER: Double **t** is like a large **u**. Join out of the crossbar.

Betty Kitty Patty · to Toto

1 LOOK
2 PLAN
3 PRACTICE

Anton Benito Otto

MmMmMmMm
MmMmMm

ta ts · Bets Santa Stanley

✏ Circle one of your best joins out of **t**.

t⃗ tl
horizontal swing up

NOTE: Avoid diagonal when joining out of **t** into ascenders of **l, h, b,** and **k.**

th

tl th · Ethel Kathy Matthew

OPTION: Lift before ascenders after **t.**

tl th · Ethel Kathy tl

OPTION: Lift before **e** after **t.**

NOTE: Write **t** and **e** close together. AVOID a gap between **t** and **e.**

te · Pete Peter te

OPTION: Join into **e** out of the first stroke of **t.**

te · Pete Peter te

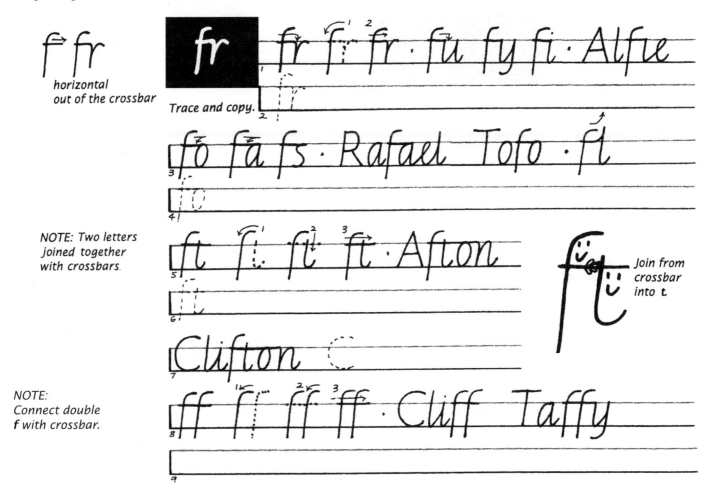

f⃗ fr

**horizontal
out of the crossbar**

fr *Trace and copy.*

fr fr fr · fu fy fi · Alfie

fo fa fs · Rafael Tofo · ft

NOTE: Two letters
joined together
with crossbars.

ft ft ft ft · Afton

*Join from
crossbar
into* **t**

Clifton C

NOTE:
Connect double
f with crossbar.

ff ff ff ff · Cliff Taffy

REVIEW: On the line below write Anton, Kathy, Rafael, and Taffy.

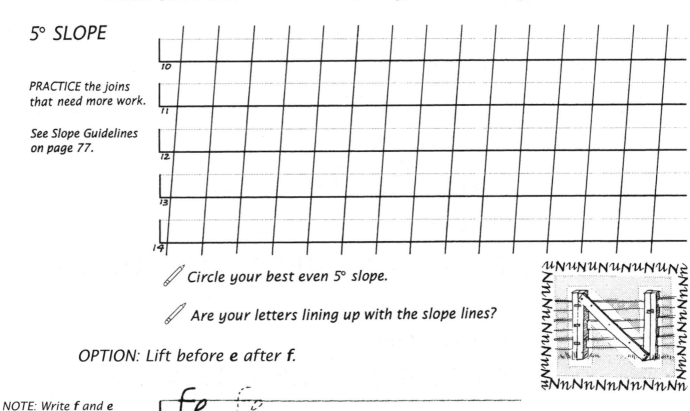

5° SLOPE

PRACTICE the joins
that need more work.

See Slope Guidelines
on page 77.

✏ Circle your best even 5° slope.

✏ Are your letters lining up with the slope lines?

OPTION: Lift before e after f.

NOTE: Write **f** and **e**
close together.

fe

w⃗ wn   vn wn

horizontal out of v and w

vn wn · vn wn · vr wr

Trace and copy.

vn

Towner · vu wu vy wy vi wi

Join with a horizontal on the waistline.

vi

Gavin Kevin Xavier

REMINDER: Use either the sharp angle bottom of **v** and **w** or the soft angle bottom of **v** and **w**.

vo wo va wa · Aviva

vu

Eva Sawa Yvonne

✏ Circle one of your best joins out of **v** and out of **w**.

OPTION: Join out of **v** and **w** into **l** and **h**.

NOTE: Avoid vl

vl wl wh · Nowles vl

OPTION: Lift after **v** and **w** before **l** and **h**.

vl wl wh · Newlin vl

OPTION: Join into **e** out of **v** and **w**.

ve we · Eve Dave Olive Arwenita

ve

NOTE: When lifting between letters, be sure to keep letters close together.

OPTION: Lift before **e** after **v** and **w**.

ve we · Sven Gwen Steve Yves

ve

$\overrightarrow{x}$ xu

horizontal

xu

Trace and copy.

xu · xu xy xi · Alexis

Maxine Maximo Roxy

M

xo xa xs · Lexa

Xa

Join out of **x** at the waistline.

✏ Circle one of your best joins out of **x**.

OPTION: Join out of **x** into **t** and **l**.

NOTE: Avoid xt xl

xt xl · Dexter Huxley

xt

OPTION: Lift after **x** before **t** and **l**.

NOTE: When lifting between letters, be sure to keep letters close together.

xt xl · Dexter Huxley

xt

OPTION: Join into **e** out of **x**.

xe · Alexei

xe

OPTION: Lift before **e** after **x**.

xe · Alexei

xe

REVIEW: JOIN 5

[1] LOOK at your writing.

[2] Pick the joins that need work. Compare them with the models. PLAN how to make joins more like the models.

[3] PRACTICE those joins.

Write Joan, Tony, Katy, Stanley, Rafael, Afton, Eva, Dave, Gwen, Maxine, and Dexter.

JOIN 6: DIAGONAL OUT OF r

Join 6 is a short diagonal line out of r into all letters except f.
(Optional join into z.)

r̃ rn
diagonal

rn

Trace and copy.

rn · rn rm rr rx

Join out of r with
a very short
diagonal.

NOTE: Be sure to bend
r before joining.

rn

AVOID rn looking
like m rn

Arne Carmen · ru ry ri rp

rv rw · Ariel Arve Boris

Cherie Chris Erin Hari

Karim Kerry Larry Mary

NOTE: The join out of r
needs more practice
than any other join.
Legibility depends on it
being done well.

OPTIONAL JOIN

ro ra rc rd rs rz · Ira

LOOK at your writing.

PLAN how to make the
letters that need more
work more like the
models.

PRACTICE on lined
paper.

Aarón Zara Jorge

Laura Marc Sara

r͏ r͏e

diagonal into e

re · Dolores Drew Pierre

re

REMINDER:
*You may use Join 2 to join into **n, m, r,** and **x.***

r͏e

Join out of r just below the waistline.

OPTIONAL JOIN

Warren Warren

W

r͏ r͏t r͏l

diagonal swing up into ascender

rt rt rt · Art Bart Burt

rt

rt rh rb rk · Barb Carl

rt

Dirk Kirk Mark

D

✎ Circle some of your best joins out of **r.**

✎ Are you joining out of **r** with a short diagonal line?   Yes____   No____

REVIEW: JOIN 6   *Write Chris, Mary, Pierre, Laura, Marc, Warren, Art, Carl, & Kirk.*

1 LOOK

2 PLAN

3 PRACTICE

OPTION: Lift after **r.**

*NOTE: When lifting after **r,** keep letters close together*

ra rb rc rd re rf rg rh ri rj rk

ra

rl rm rn ro rp rq rr rs rt ru rv

rt

rw rx ry rz rw

JOIN 7: HORIZONTAL TO DIAGONAL

Join 7 is a horizontal line at the baseline blending into a diagonal line.
Follow back out of **s**, **b**, and **p** and join into all letters except **f** and **z**.

s sn

horizontal
to diagonal

sn   sn · sn sm · Kasni

Trace and copy.

su sy si sp sw st sl sh sk

Follow back out of s
into diagonal join.

Ashley Iskemu Elsie

Kirsten Leslie Makesi

Moshe Susie Yoshi · so ss

se · Cherise Else Jessie José

1. LOOK
2. PLAN
3. PRACTICE

Circle one of your best joins out of **s**.

OPTION: Lift after **s**.

NOTE:
When lifting
between letters,
be sure to keep
letters close
together.

sn sm su sy si sp sv

sw st sl sh sk so se ss

Susie Leslie José

b br
horizontal to diagonal

br

Trace and copy.

br · br Abram · bu by bi

bl bb · Abby Barbie Bobby

Follow back out of b into diagonal join.

by

Debby Pablo Ruby

bo bs · Babs Deborah Noboru

be · Abe Alberta Ebenezer

Circle one of your best joins out of **b**.

OPTION: Lift after **b**.

NOTE: When lifting between letters, be sure to keep letters close together.

br bu by bi bl bb bo be bs · Abby

Barbie Pablo Ruby Abe Bobby

Deborah Noboru

1 LOOK

2 PLAN

3 PRACTICE

p pr
horizontal out of p to diagonal

pr Trace and copy.

pr · pr · April · pu py pi

pp pl ph · Aphra Apu Happy

Christopher Ralph

ph
Follow back out of p.

po ps · Aponi · pe Hope

✏ Circle one of your best joins out of **p**.

✏ Are you following back out of **b**, **p** and **s**, and joining with a diagonal line?

Yes____ No____

OPTION: Lift after **p**.

NOTE:
When lifting between letters, be sure to keep letters close together.

pr pu py pi pp pl ph · Aphra

Apu Happy Christopher Ralph

REVIEW: JOIN 7 *On the lines below write Cherise, Noboru, and Christopher.*

① LOOK

② PLAN

③ PRACTICE

JOIN 8: DIAGONAL TO HORIZONTAL

Join 8 is a diagonal line from the baseline blending into a horizontal line at the waistline. Join into **a**, **c**, **d**, **g**, **q**, and **s**.

a a ã

diagonal
to horizontal

Trace and copy.

aa · aa ca da ea ha ia

ka la ma na ua za · Alana

NOTE:
Close up the top of **a** so that **a** doesn't look like **u**.

a u

Join from the diagonal to the horizontal top of **a**.

Cordelia Diana

REMINDER:
a has a flat head

a

Juana Mia Nina Omar

AVOID pointed head on **a**

a

sa ba pa Barbara Lisa Papa

✏ Circle one of your best joins into **a**.

OPTION: Lift before **a** from the baseline

NOTE:
When lifting between letters, be sure to keep letters close together.

aa ba ca da ea ha ia ka la ma

na pa sa ua za · Lisa

Juana Alana Diana

a *ac*

**diagonal
to horizontal**

Trace and copy.

ac *ac · ac cc ec ic uc sc*

ac

Alicia Jack Oscar

**Join from the
diagonal to the
horizontal top of c.**

AVOID wave

ac

Michael Michelle Rachel

M

✏ Circle one of your best joins into **c**.

a *ad*

**diagonal
to horizontal**

ad *ad · ad dd ed id ld nd*

ad

NOTE:
Close up the top of
d so that d doesn't
look like **cl**.

d d

ud · Alexander Amanda

ud

① LOOK

② PLAN

③ PRACTICE

Eddie Heidi Linda Sid Todd

✏ Circle one of your best joins into **d**.

OPTION: Lift before **c** and **d** from the baseline.

NOTE:
When lifting
between letters,
be sure to keep
letters close
together.

ac cc ec ic uc sc

ac

ad dd ed id ld nd

ad

a/ a͠g
diagonal
to horizontal

ag a͠g · ag eg ig ng ug sg

Trace and copy.

a͠g

NOTE:
Close up the top of
g and **q** so that **g** and
q don't look like **y**.

g y q y

Angela Ingrid Meg Santiago

✏ Circle one of your best joins into **g**.

a/ a͠q
diagonal
to horizontal

aq a͠q · aq eq iq uq · Aataq

aq

✏ Circle one of your best joins into **q**.

a/ a͠s
diagonal
to horizontal

as a͠s · as es is us ss

Join from the
diagonal to the
horizontal top of **s**.

es

Cassie Jess Justin Nelson

Leslie Susan Saskia

OPTION: Lift before **g**, **q**, and **s**.

NOTE:
When lifting
between letters,
be sure to keep
letters close
together.

ag eg ig ug aq eq iq uq as es is us

ag

Meg Aataq Jess M

REVIEW: JOIN 8

On the lines below write Aataq, Linda, Michael, Meg, and Susan.

1
2

LOOK at your writing.   ✏ *Circle one of your best diagonal to horizontal joins.*

REVIEW: GETTY-DUBAY CURSIVE ITALIC JOINS & OPTIONS

NOTE:
Joins 1 to 8 used
in this pangram.

A quick brown fox jumps over the lazy dog. A

NOTE:
Joins 2 to 8 used
in this pangram.

A quick brown fox jumps over the lazy dog. A

NOTE:
Joins 2, 3, & 5 as
well as all optional
lifts used in this
pangram.

A quick brown fox jumps over the lazy dog. A

Basic italic:

A quick brown fox jumps over the lazy dog. A

2 PLAN
3 PRACTICE

Write this pangram using your choice of joins & lifts.

NOTE: Have you
made an improvement
in your handwriting?
Pick a page of your
best handwriting to
put in your Student
Portfolio.

LIFTS: Lift before *f* and after *g, j, q,* and *y.*

Lift before *z* after a letter ending at the baseline.

af az

space letters close together

af az Trace and copy.

af ef if of uf · Rafael

NOTE: AVOID gap

a̋z

az ez iz oz uz · Aziza Bozzo

REMINDER: See Join 5 for the horizontal join into z.

Beatriz Kazuo Liza Suzo

✏ Are you lifting before *f* and *z*?   Yes____   No____

✏ Circle your best spacing with a lift between letters.

ga ja qu ya Anya Elijah

NOTE:
Joins are natural spacers. When letters are not joined, place letters close together to avoid gaps.

Enrique George Gregory Sonja

Jacqueline Margaret Miguel

✏ Circle your best spacing with a lift between letters.

NOTE: Close up the top of *a, d, g, q,* and *o.*

AVOID:
a and *o* read as *u,*
g and *q* read as *y,*
and *d* read as *cl.*

a u · d cl · g y · q y · o v
u?   cl?   y?   y?   u?

SIZE: 5mm body height; 7½ mm capital and ascender height and descender length

capital and ascender height →

body height 5mm

descender length →

Body height is now 5mm.

B

REVIEW: GETTY-DUBAY CURSIVE ITALIC JOINS, LIFTS & OPTIONS

Trace and copy.

JOIN 1 *diagonal*
an am ar ax an

JOIN 2 *diagonal*
swing up
au ay ai aj ap au

at al ah ab ak at

av aw av

OPTION:
an am ar ax an

JOIN 3 *diagonal* OPTION:
start back
ao as ao

JOIN 4 *diagonal* OPTION:
into e
ae ae ae

JOIN 5 *horizontal*
ou tu fu ou

vu wu xu vu

JOIN 6 *diagonal* OPTION:
into r
ru ru ru

JOIN 7 *horizontal* OPTION:
to diagonal
su bu pu su   *su bu pu*

JOIN 8 *diagonal to* OPTION:
horizontal
aa ac ad aa   *aa ac ad*

OPTION:
ag aq as ag   *ag aq as*

LIFTS *before f & z*
and after
g, j, q, & y
af az af

gu ju qu yu gu

Copy the models and
practice on lined
paper.
abcdefghijklmnopqrstuvwxyz

a

Trace and copy.

halfway

1 *Capital and ascender height*

halfway

2 *and descender length are*

3 *halfway between lines.*

4

5

6

Write your signature using cursive italic.

7 *Name:*

Write your address, name of your school and city, and names of your relatives using cursive italic.

8 *Address:*

9

10 *School:*

11 *City:*

12 *Grandmother*

13 *G*

14 *Grandfather*

15 *G*

16 *Uncle U*

17 *Aunt A*

18

Are your capitals, ascenders and descenders the correct height & length?   Yes ___   No ___

waistline

19

20

BASELINE ONLY: Write on the baseline and imagine where the waistline is. (It is halfway between the baselines.) This is like writing on wide-ruled notebook paper.

21

22

23

PANGRAM: *A sentence containing all the letters in the alphabet.*

ABC··XYZ

Trace and copy.

A quick brown fox jumps over
the lazy dog. A

5° SLOPE

Use the slope lines to help you write with an even slope. In the best writing all letters slope the same way. Use slope lines under lined paper. See Slope Guidelines on page 77.

Autumn was quiet except for
A
the crunch of golden brown
leaves dizzy from their journey
back to earth.

✏ *Are you using a 5° slope?   Yes___   No___*

NOTE: HYPHEN
Use a short dash when separating syllables of a word on different lines.

2-word numbers below 100 have a hyphen.
e.g. twenty-six

Including all twenty-six alphabet letters often requires making
use of very jazzy words.
I

1 LOOK at your writing.   ✏ *Circle one of your best 5° slope words.   Write your own pangram below.*

2 PLAN how to write with an even slope.

3 PRACTICE

GETTY-DUBAY NUMERALS

NUMERALS: *The size of numerals is one body height.*

Trace and copy.

0 — Are
1 — your
2 — numerals
3 — one
4 — body
5
6 — height
7 — ?   Yes___
8 — No___
9

0 zero · 1 one · 2 two · 3 three

4 four · 5 five · 6 six · 7 seven

8 eight · 9 nine · 10 ten · 11 eleven

12 twelve · 13 thirteen · 14 fourteen

15 fifteen · 16 sixteen · 17 seventeen

18 eighteen · 19 nineteen · 20 twenty

30 thirty · 40 forty · 50 fifty

60 sixty · 70 seventy · 80 eighty

90 ninety · 100 one hundred

1000 one thousand · one million

OPTION: Write numerals the same height as capitals.

0123456789 0

GETTY-DUBAY BASIC ITALIC CAPITALS & CURSIVE ITALIC CAPITALS

EGYPTIAN HIEROGLYPH	PHOENICIAN LETTER	GREEK LETTER	ROMAN LETTER	BASIC ITALIC CAPITAL	CURSIVE ITALIC CAPITAL Trace and copy.

OX

5° slope

1st stroke: curve exit serif

3rd stroke: extended entrance of crossbar

Write other names beginning with A.

Alice Alan Adrienne Antonio

NOTE:
Basic italic capitals may be used with cursive italic lower-case if preferred to cursive capitals.

✏ Circle your best **A.**

✏ Are you ending your first stroke of **A** with a curve exit serif?   Yes___ No___

HOUSE

2nd stroke: curve entrance serif

Brian Belinda Benjamin Betty

Write other names beginning with B.

LOOK at your writing. Pick your best letter. Answer the question.

Pick the letters that need work. Compare them with the models. PLAN how to make the letters that need more work more like the models.

PRACTICE those letters on the lines below and on lined paper.

✏ Circle your best **B.**

✏ Are you beginning your second stroke of **B** with a curve entrance serif?

Yes___ No___

EGYPTIAN HIEROGLYPH	PHOENICIAN LETTER	GREEK LETTER	ROMAN LETTER	BASIC ITALIC CAPITAL	CURSIVE ITALIC CAPITAL Trace and copy.
⌐ CAMEL	<	C	C	C	C C

no change

Carol Carlos Catherine Claude

Write other names beginning with C.

✏️ Circle your best **C.**

✏️ Does your Cursive **C** look like the Basic **C**?   Yes____ No____

| ⫛⫛⫛ DOOR | △ | ▷ | D | D | D D |

2nd stroke: curve entrance serif

David Darlene Duane Donna

Write other names beginning with D.

1️⃣ LOOK at your writing. Pick your best letter. Answer the question.

✏️ Circle your best **D.**

2️⃣ Pick the letters that need work. Compare them with the models. PLAN how to make the letters that need more work look more like the models.

✏️ Are you beginning your second stroke of **D** with a curve entrance serif?

Yes____ No____

3️⃣ PRACTICE those letters here and on lined paper.

EGYPTIAN HIEROGLYPH	PHOENICIAN LETTER	GREEK LETTER	ROMAN LETTER	BASIC ITALIC CAPITAL	CURSIVE ITALIC CAPITAL Trace and copy.

BEHOLD

2nd stroke: curve entrance serif

Ellen Edward Elisa Ethan

Write other names beginning with E.

🖊 Circle your best **E.**

🖊 Are you beginning your second stroke of **E** with a curve entrance serif?

Yes___ No___

HOOK

2nd stroke: curve entrance serif

Francis Frances Fernando

Write other names beginning with F.

1️⃣ LOOK at your writing.   🖊 Circle your best **F.**

🖊 Are you beginning your second stroke of **F** with a curve entrance serif?

Yes___ No___

2️⃣ PLAN which letters need work. How will you make them look more like the models?

3️⃣ PRACTICE the letters that need more work.

	PHOENICIAN LETTER	GREEK LETTER	ROMAN LETTER	BASIC ITALIC CAPITAL	CURSIVE ITALIC CAPITAL Trace and copy.

(Added in the 3rd century B.C.
The Romans added a bar to C to form G.)

G   G   G   G

changes to one-stroke:
curve exit serif

Greta Gregory Grace Glenn

Write other names
beginning with G.

✏️ Circle your best **G**.

✏️ Are you using a one-stroke **G**?   Yes___   No___

NOTE: 2nd stroke
begins higher

H   H   H   H   H   H   H

FENCE

1st stroke: sharp angle
entrance serif,
curve exit serif

2nd stroke: curve
entrance serif begins
slightly higher

3rd stroke: extended
crossbar

Write other names
beginning with H.

Helge Hannah Harold Heather

✏️ Circle your best **H**.

✏️ Are you beginning the second stroke of **H** slightly higher than the capital
height?   Yes___   No___

▢1 LOOK at your writing.

▢2 PLAN which letters
need work. How will
you make them look
more like the models?

▢3 PRACTICE the letters
that need more work.

EGYPTIAN HIEROGLYPH	PHOENICIAN LETTER	GREEK LETTER	ROMAN LETTER	BASIC ITALIC CAPITAL	CURSIVE ITALIC CAPITAL Trace and copy.

I

changes to one-stroke: horizontal entrance serif and exit serif

Isabel Irving Ingrid Ivan

Write other names beginning with I.

✏ Circle your best **I**.

✏ Are you beginning and ending your **I** with horizontal serifs?

Yes____ No____

(Added in the 16th century.)

J

one stroke: horizontal entrance serif

Joseph Julia Jonathan Juanita

Write other names beginning with J.

① LOOK at your writing. ✏ Circle your best **J**.

✏ Are you beginning your **J** with a horizontal entrance serif? Yes____ No____

② PLAN which letters need work. How will you make them look more like the models?

③ PRACTICE those letters.

EGYPTIAN HIEROGLYPH	PHOENICIAN LETTER	GREEK LETTER	ROMAN LETTER	BASIC ITALIC CAPITAL	CURSIVE ITALIC CAPITAL Trace and copy.

1st stroke: sharp angle entrance serif, curve exit serif

2nd stroke: curve exit serif

Karen Kirk Kumiko 久美子 Keith

Write other names beginning with K.

✏ Circle your best **K**.

✏ Are you beginning your K with a sharp angle entrance serif?

Yes___ No___

one stroke: curve entrance serif, short exit serif

Luis Louisa Lewis Lucinda

Write other names beginning with L.

1️⃣ LOOK at your writing.

✏ Circle your best **L**.

✏ Are you beginning your L with a curve entrance serif? Yes___ No___

2️⃣ PLAN how to make letters more like models.

3️⃣ PRACTICE the letters that need more work.

EGYPTIAN HIEROGLYPH	PHOENICIAN LETTER	GREEK LETTER	ROMAN LETTER	BASIC ITALIC CAPITAL	CURSIVE ITALIC CAPITAL Trace and copy.

WATER

1st stroke: curve exit serif

Maria Manuel Mona Miguel

Write other names beginning with M.

🖊 Circle your best **M**.

🖊 Are you ending your first stroke of M with a curve exit serif?

Yes___ No___

FISH

1st stroke: curve exit serif

3rd stroke: curve entrance serif begins slightly higher

Nathan Nancy Nelson Nora

Write other names beginning with N.

1️⃣ LOOK at your writing. 🖊 Circle your best **N**.

🖊 Are you beginning the third stroke of N slightly higher than the capital height? Yes___ No___

2️⃣ PLAN how to make the letters that need more work more like the models.

3️⃣ PRACTICE here the letters that need work.

EGYPTIAN HIEROGLYPH	PHOENICIAN LETTER	GREEK LETTER	ROMAN LETTER	BASIC ITALIC CAPITAL	CURSIVE ITALIC CAPITAL Trace and copy.

EYE

no changes

Olivia Olaf Ophelia Octavius

Write other names beginning with O.

✎ Circle your best **O**.

✎ Does your Cursive **O** look like the Basic O?   Yes____ No____

MOUTH

2nd stroke: curve entrance serif

Patrick Patricia Percy Pamela

Write other names beginning with P.

🧊 LOOK

🧊 PLAN

🧊 PRACTICE

✎ Circle your best **P**.

✎ Are you beginning your second stroke of **P** with a curve entrance serif?

Yes____ No____

EGYPTIAN HIEROGLYPH	PHOENICIAN LETTER	GREEK LETTER	ROMAN LETTER	BASIC ITALIC CAPITAL	CURSIVE ITALIC CAPITAL Trace and copy.
φ	φ KNOT	Q	Q	Q	Q · Q Q Q

2nd stroke: short exit serif

Quinlan Quincy Queenie Quang

Write other names beginning with Q.

✎ Circle your best **Q**.

✎ Are you ending your second stroke of **Q** with a short exit serif?

Yes___ No___

🦅 HEAD	◁	P	R	R R	R · R R R R R

2nd stroke: curve entrance serif

3rd stroke: curve exit serif

Robert Raquel Ricardo Ruth

Write other names beginning with R.

1️⃣ LOOK at your writing. Pick your best letter. Answer the question.

✎ Circle your best **R**.

✎ Are you beginning your second stroke of **R** with a curve entrance serif?

Yes___ No___

2️⃣ Pick the letters that need work. Compare them with the models. PLAN how to make the letters that need more work look more like the models.

3️⃣ PRACTICE those letters here and on lined paper.

EGYPTIAN HIEROGLYPH	PHOENICIAN LETTER	GREEK LETTER	ROMAN LETTER	BASIC ITALIC CAPITAL	CURSIVE ITALIC CAPITAL Trace and copy.

TOOTH

no changes

Sandra Samuel Santiago Susan

Write other names beginning with S.

✏ Circle your best **S**.

✏ Does your Cursive **S** look like the Basic **S**?   Yes____ No____

MARK/SIGN

2nd stroke: curve entrance serif

Thomas Teresa Theo Tamara

Write other names beginning with T.

▢ **LOOK**

▢ **PLAN**

▢ **PRACTICE**

✏ Circle your best **T**.

✏ Are you beginning the top of your **T** with a curve entrance serif?

Yes____ No____

PHOENICIAN LETTER	GREEK LETTER	ROMAN LETTER	BASIC ITALIC CAPITAL	CURSIVE ITALIC CAPITAL Trace and copy.

(Added in the 16th century.)

U

one-stroke: soft angle entrance serif

Ursula Ulysses Urania Uriah

Write other names beginning with U.

🖊 Circle your best **U**.

🖊 Are you beginning your **U** with a soft angle entrance serif?   Yes____   No____

Y   F   V   HOOK/NAIL

V

one-stroke: curve entrance serif

Victor Vivian Vincent Violetta

Write other names beginning with V.

1️⃣ LOOK at your writing.

🖊 Circle your best **V**.

2️⃣ PLAN how to make letters more like models.

🖊 Are you beginning your **V** with a curve entrance serif?   Yes____   No____

3️⃣ PRACTICE the letters that need more work.

PHOENICIAN LETTER	GREEK LETTER	ROMAN LETTER	BASIC ITALIC CAPITAL	CURSIVE ITALIC CAPITAL Trace and copy.

(Added in the 11th century.)

one-stroke: curve entrance serif

Wilma William Winona Waldo

Write other names beginning with W.

✏ Circle your best **W**.

✏ Are you beginning your **W** with a curve entrance serif?   Yes____ No____

PROP

1st stroke: entrance serif and exit serif

Xerxes Xina Xavier Ximena

Write other names beginning with X.

1️⃣ LOOK at your writing.

✏ Circle your best **X**.

✏ Are you beginning and ending your first stroke of X with curve serifs?

Yes____ No____

2️⃣ PLAN which letters need work.

3️⃣ PRACTICE those letters here.

EGYPTIAN HIEROGLYPH	PHOENICIAN LETTER	GREEK LETTER	ROMAN LETTER	BASIC ITALIC CAPITAL	CURSIVE ITALIC CAPITAL
Y	Y	Y	Y	Y · y y	y y
	HOOK/NAIL			Y	y y

changes to one-stroke: soft angle entrance serif, curve exit serif

Yolanda Yon Yvonne Yoshi

Write other names beginning with Y.

✏ Circle your best **Y**.

✏ Are you beginning your one-stroke **Y** with a soft angle entrance serif?

Yes____ No____

| Z | Z | Z | Z | Z · Z Z | Z Z |
| | SICKLE/WEAPON | | | Z. Z Z. | Z Z. |

one-stroke: short entrance serif and exit serif

Zeke Zada Zachary Zelenka

Write other names beginning with Z.

✏ Circle your best **Z**.

✏ Are you beginning and ending your **Z** with short entrance serifs?

Yes____ No____

▢ 1 LOOK
▢ 2 PLAN
▢ 3 PRACTICE

NOTE:
For further Cursive Italic Capital assessment, see INSTRUCTION MANUAL.

REVIEW: GETTY-DUBAY CURSIVE ITALIC CAPITALS & LOWERCASE JOINS

SIZE: *Height of capitals & ascenders and length of descenders.*

capital and ascender height

Aa ana *Bb nb* or *na* *Cc nc* or *bn* *Dd nd* or *nc* or *nd*

descender length

Ee ne or *ne* *Ff nf* *Gg ng* or *ng* *Hh nh*

REMINDER: *Two capitals reach slightly higher than capital height. Four capitals have descenders.*

HN · GJQY

Ii ini *Jj nj* *Kk knk* or *knk* *Ll lnl*

NOTE: *Basic italic capitals may be used with cursive italic lowercase if preferred to cursive capitals.*

Mm nm or *mnm* *Nn nn* or *nnn* *Oo no* *Pp np* or *pn*

NOTE: *For review of optional joins and lifts see pages 44 & 46.*

Qq nq or *nq* *Rr nr* or *rnr* *Ss ns* or *sns* *Tt nt*

Uu nu *Vv nv* *Ww nw* *Xx nx* or *nx*

Yy ny *Zz nz*

LOOK *at your writing. Answer the question.* *Are your capitals the correct capital height?* Yes____ No____

Pick the letters that need work. Compare them with the models. PLAN how to make the letters that need more work look more like the models.

PRACTICE those letters here and on lined paper.

Write your signature using cursive italic.

PUNCTUATION: Quotation marks, question mark, exclamation mark and apostrophe begin at the capital height. Comma begins at the baseline where a period is made.

capital height
"Hi, how are you?" she said.

capital height
"I'm fine, thank you!" he replied.

Trace and copy.

AMPERSAND: The ampersand is an abbreviation for 'and.' It is a shape derived from the letters e and t. 'Et' is the latin word for 'and.'

You & I are friends.

E and T combine to form the ampersand.

Another ampersand (two strokes) & & &

SLOPE: 5° slope

Sunday, Monday, Tuesday,

Slope lines are included to help keep an even slope.

For individualized slope line see Slope Guidelines on page 77.

Wednesday, Thursday, Friday &

NOTE: This decoration is called the 'cosmic flower'.

Saturday & January, February,

March, April, May, June, July,

1 LOOK at your writing.

August, September, October,

2 PLAN how to make letters more like models.

3 PRACTICE on lined paper.

November & December &

NOTE: See Slope Guidelines on page 77.

Circle one of your best areas with an even slope.

GETTY-DUBAY CURSIVE ITALIC WRITING PRACTICE

SPACING: Use even spacing in words.

VOWEL SOUNDS:
AI: long A
AY: long A

ai rain   ay day   -eigh weigh

PHONOGRAM: -EIGH
(see definition below)

ai   ay   eigh

HOMOPHONES:
Homophones are words that sound the same but have different meanings and usually different spellings.

ate, eight · way, weigh, whey

a.

wait, weight · sail, sale

w

POEM: COUPLET
A couplet has two rhyming lines of the same length.

Rain, rain go away,
Come again another day.

R

C

When lifting are you keeping letters close together?   Yes___   No___

PRACTICE even letter spacing.

PHONOGRAMS:
A phonogram is a vowel sound plus a consonant sound. It is often less than a syllable. It needs an initial consonant or blend to make it a word.

-ear bear   -air fair   -are care

ear

HOMOPHONES:

stare, stair · hare, hair · fair, fare

s

REMINDER: Join into e at the center when connecting from the baseline.

Please pare a pair of pears.

P

Circle your best join into e from the baseline.

PRACTICE the joins that need more work.

NOTE: See THE NEW READING TEACHER'S BOOK OF LISTS, 333 Homographs, pp. 12-20 and Phonograms, pp. 124-133.

VOWEL SOUNDS:
EE:long E
EA:long E
Y:long E

ee bee ea each   y happy

ee

HOMOPHONES:

be, bee · deer, dear · heel, heal

b

meet, meat · see, sea · week, weak

m

VOWEL SOUND:
EA: short E sound

HOMOPHONE:

ea heavy bread · red, read

ea

PHONOGRAMS:

-ee see · -eed seed · -eek seek

ee

NOTE: Keep using the carefully practiced letter shapes.

-eel wheel · -eem seem · -een seen

eel

-eep sleep · -eer deer · -eet feet

eep

POEM: HAIKU
Haiku is a Japanese poem form. There are three lines and 17 syllables. The first and third lines have five syllables and the second line has seven syllables.

In the city fields
Contemplating cherry trees
Strangers are like friends.

Issa

NOTE: The poet's name is on the fourth line. The last letter of the poet's name lines up with the last letter of the longest line of the poem.

Is the height of your capitals and ascenders halfway between the waistline and the baseline above it?   Yes___   No___

SILENT E: The sound of the vowel changes when silent E is added.

car, care · fin, fine · mad, made

c

fir, fire · hug, huge · rob, robe

f

PHONOGRAMS:

-ie pie -igh high -y July -im dim

ie

-ime dime -in kin -ine dine

ime

-ind wind -ink wink -ing wing

ind

-ide wide -ill will -ilt wilt

ide

POEM: ACROSTIC
An acrostic is a poem in which the first letter of each line forms a word. This one is FIVE by David Greenberg (from TEACHING POETRY TO CHILDREN).

First day of school
Inside we walked
Viewing the walls
Everyone gasped

Write your own acrostic. Choose any word - perhaps your own name.

N
A
M
E

Line it up vertically.

Start the first word of each line with the letter on that line.

Copy poem or write your own acrostic poem.

REMINDER: Tap your index finger on the pencil three times to help avoid pinching. See Pencil Hold on page vi.

Are you holding your pencil lightly? Yes___ No___

VOWEL SOUNDS:
OA: long O
OW: long O

oa road coast ow row know

oa

HOMOPHONES:

toe, tow · no, know · row, row

t

VOWEL SOUNDS:
AU: broad O
AW: broad O

au August dinosaur aw draw

au

POEM: CINQUAIN
A cinquain is a five line poem beginning and ending with one word and increasing by one word from the second to the fourth lines.

Letters

Many shapes

Sounding and grouping

Waiting to be arranged

Poem

Topic: 1 word

Description: 2 words

Action: 3 words

Feeling: 4 words

Summary: 1 word

SIZE REMINDER:
Height of capitals and ascenders is halfway between waistline and baseline above. Length of descenders is halfway between baseline and waistline below.

1. LOOK at your writing. Are your capitals and ascenders the correct height?   Yes____   No____

2. Which letter sizes need to be improved?
How will you improve them?

3. PRACTICE
Write your own cinquain here.

VOWEL SOUNDS:
OO: short OO
OO: long OO

oo good book oo cool bamboo

oo

PHONOGRAMS:

-oo zoo -ood food -ool school

oo

REMINDER: JOIN 5
Join out of *o* with a
horizontal line at the
waistline. (Avoid a
scoop.)

-oom room -oon noon -oot root

oom

-ew new knew -ue blue glue

ew

POEM: LIMERICK A limerick is a light or humorous verse form of five lines. The first, second, and
fifth lines follow one rhyme and the third and fourth lines follow another rhyme.

There was an old man from Peru

Who dreamed he was eating his shoe.

In the midst of the night

He awoke in a fright

And—good grief! It was perfectly true!

Anonymous

NOTE: This is tight spacing
Write your letters close together.

If you were not able to
fit the words in the
space provided, use
tighter spacing next
time. Sometimes you
must adjust your
writing to fit the space
provided.

Using tight spacing, are you able to fit the second and fifth lines of the
limerick in the space provided?   Yes____   No____

VOWEL SOUNDS:
OI: OI dipthong
OY: OI dipthong

oi oil noise   oy oyster enjoy

oi

What noise annoys an oyster?

W

VOWEL SOUNDS:
OU: OU dipthong
OW: OW dipthong

ou south flour   ow now flower

ou

scatter seeds	female pig	weapon for shooting arrows	forward part of a ship	bend in greeting	line	use oars to move a boat	noisy fight

HOMOGRAPHS:
Homographs are words that are spelled the same but have different meanings and origins.

sow, sow · bow, bow, bow · row, row, row

s

PHONOGRAMS:

-out shout   -ouse house

out

-outh mouth   -ound round

outh

FORMULA POEM:
by David Greenburg

Nothing is an old empty house

N

Trace and copy.

N

Compose and write your own poem.
"Nothing is . . . "

NOTE:
The poet doesn't use periods for this type of poem.

Friendship is being able to talk to

someone

Trace and copy.

Compose and write your own poem.
"Friendship is . . . "

NOTE: See THE NEW READING TEACHER'S BOOK OF LISTS, 333 Homographs, pp. 12-20.

VOWEL SOUNDS:
AR: AR sound
OR: OR sound

ar large jar   or order form for

ar

ER: R sound
IR: R sound
UR: R sound

er camera   ir stir   ur surface

er

PHONOGRAMS:

-eak speak   -eal heal   -eat neat

eak

-eam beam   -ean bean   -ear hear

eam

CONSONANT SOUNDS:
C: S sound
G: J sound

c circle center   g gym large

c

CH: digraph
PHONOGRAMS:

ch change   -atch watch   -ack back

ch

REMINDER: The
question mark is the
same height as the
capitals.

Watch which backpack?

W

CONSONANT SOUNDS:
KN: N sound
Q: KW sound

kn know knock   qu quiet quick

kn

COMPOUND WORDS: Two words are blended into one word.

wheelchair · birthday · handwriting

w

CONTRACTIONS: A word group is shortened by leaving out one or two letters. An apostrophe takes the place of the missing letters. (let us—let's; can not—can't; I am—I'm; we will—we'll)

Let's go. I can't. I'm tired. We'll stay.

CONSONANT SOUNDS:
PH: F sound
SH: digraph

ph phone alphabet sh shape

ph

TONGUE TWISTER:

She sells seashells by the seashore.

S

CONSONANT SOUNDS:
TH: digraph voiceless
TH: digraph voiced

th thank truth th the smooth

th

WH: digraph
(HW blend)

wh Which white whale whistled?

wh

TONGUE TWISTER:

Which watches are Swiss wrist-watches? *w*

REMINDER: Join out of *t* and *w* into *h* with a horizontal swing up into the ascender. (See Join 5)

✏ Circle one of your best **th** joins and one of your best **wh** joins.

SPECIAL ASSIGNMENT: WRITE A LETTER

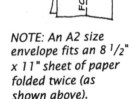
LETTER

Write a letter to a relative, a friend, or a pen-pal. You may be writing a 'thank you' letter, replying to a letter you have received, or asking an answer to a question.

ROUGH DRAFT: Compose your letter in pencil. Use the 5mm guidelines on page 80 under a sheet of paper or use lined paper.

CHECK YOUR WORDING: Edit for capitals, spelling and punctuation.

FINAL COPY: Use your best handwriting for your final copy. Take your time. Write your final copy with a pencil or pen.

ENVELOPE: Address the envelope using your best handwriting.
On the first line write the name of the person you are writing to.
On the second line write the person's house number and street name (apartment number, Post Office Box number, etc.).
On the third line write the city, state, and zip code. (Add country if needed.)

FOLD

FO LD

In the upper left hand corner write your return address.

NOTE: An A2 size envelope fits an 8 1/2" x 11" sheet of paper folded twice (as shown above).

For lines on which to write a letter and for an envelope template see INSTRUCTION MANUAL.

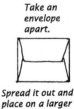
Take an envelope apart.

Spread it out and place on a larger piece of paper.

Trace around the edge. Cut out the new envelope. Fold envelope. Glue or tape to hold together.

glue or tape

Getty-Dubay Cursive Italic

CONSONANT SOUNDS:
BR: BR blend
CR: CR blend
DR: DR blend

br branch cr create dr dream

br

FR: FR blend
GR: GR blend
PR: PR blend

fr fresh gr green pr practice

fr

TR: TR blend
TW: TW blend
BL: BL blend

tr trail tw twice bl blend

tr

CL: CL blend
FL: FL blend
GL: GL blend

cl cloud fl float gl glance

cl

SPACING BETWEEN WORDS: Leave the width of an **n** between words.

I glance at clouds floating by.

I

CONSONANT SOUNDS:
PL: PL blend
SL: SL blend
SC: SC blend

pl please sl slope sc score

pl

SK: SK blend
SM: SM blend
SN: SN blend

sk sky sm small sn snow

sk

SP: SP blend
ST: ST blend
SW: SW blend

sp space st start sw swim

sp

WR: R sound

wr I write cursive italic.

wr

LOOK at your writing. Are you leaving the width of an **n** between words?   Yes____ No____

PLAN how to make the spacing look more like the models. Circle your best spacing between words in a sentence.

PRACTICE writing using the width of an **n** between words.

CONSONANT SOUNDS:
GH: silent
NG: NG

gh high eight ng spring

gh

PHONOGRAMS:

-ang sang -ing sing -ong song

ang

-ung sung -ank sank -ink sink

ung

-unk sunk -amp lamp -imp limp

unk

-ump lump -ame came -ome come

ump

REMINDER: 5° SLOPE

TONGUE TWISTER:

A skunk sat on a stump.
The stump thunk* the skunk
stunk and the skunk thunk the
stump stunk!

✳ *'Thunk' is a made-up word.
It is used instead of 'thought'.*

NOTE:
*Joins 1 to 8 and the
one-stroke **k** are used
here.*

1 LOOK

2 PLAN

*How will you write with
an even slope?*
*See Slope Guidelines
on page 77.*

3 PRACTICE

A

NOTE:
*Joins 2 to 8, the
two-stroke **k**, and
optional lifts before
e and after **s** are
used here.*

A skunk sat on a stump. The stump
thunk* the skunk stunk and the
skunk thunk the stump stunk!

PREFIXES:

im- improve   dis-disability

im

re- return recycle un- unusual

re

FORMULA POEM:
by David Greenberg

Alone is having no one to talk to.

A

Compose and write
your own formula
poem.

Alone is

SUFFIXES:

-er teacher writer -or conductor

er

-y healthy -ly slowly finally

y

-ty safety seventy -ist violinist

ty

-ful careful -less tireless

ful

PRACTICE: Have you
made an improvement
in your handwriting?
Pick a page of your
best handwriting to
put in your Student
Portfolio.

-ness happiness -ing writing

ness

Compose and write
your own formula
poem.

Happiness is

CONGRATULATIONS! You have completed this book. You are improving your
handwriting day by day. Good Work!

As you write on your own, continue to practice good handwriting habits: even
slope, even size, and even spacing. Hooray for you and your good handwriting!

Turn to page viii and write your Post-test. Use your best cursive italic
handwriting.

READING LOOPED CURSIVE
COMPARING GETTY-DUBAY CURSIVE ITALIC WITH LOOPED CURSIVE

NOTE: letter shape, letter slope, and size of capitals, ascenders, and descenders

Look at the examples of cursive italic and looped cursive. Compare the two styles of writing. Notice the differences in letter shape, letter slope, capital height, ascender height, and descender length.

There are many styles of writing you need to be able to read. Practice reading looped cursive. To help read the looped cursive letters, each name contains both a capital letter and its lowercase version.

SHAPE:
Look at the different shapes of the looped cursive lowercase letters b, f, r, s, and z and the capital letters F, G, I, J, Q, S, T, V, X, and Z.

SLOPE:
Look at the slope difference. Cursive Italic letter slope is 5° and looped cursive is 30°.

SIZE:
Look at the size difference. Cursive italic capitals, ascenders, and descenders are 1 1/2 body heights. Looped cursive capitals, ascenders and descenders are 2 body heights.

Compare the absence of loops in cursive italic with the many loops in looped cursive. Look at how the capitals, ascenders, and descenders become tangled in the looped cursive.
Loop-free italic is easier to read.

CURSIVE ITALIC	LOOPED CURSIVE
5° slope	30° slope
Angela	Angela
Barbara	Barbara
Cecilia	Cecilia
David	David
Eugene	Eugene
Fifi	Fifi
Gregory	Gregory
Hannah	Hannah
Irving	Irving
Jojo	Jojo
Kirk	Kirk
Lillian	Lillian
Malcolm	Malcolm
Nancy	Nancy
Otto	Otto
Philippa	Philippa
Quequeg	Quequeg
Richard	Richard
Susan	Susan
Trent	Trent
Ursula	Ursula
Vivian	Vivian
Woodrow	Woodrow
Xerxes	Xerxes
Yonny	Yonny
Zanzi	Zanzi

SLOPE GUIDELINES:

A 5° letter slope is used for basic and cursive.

OPTIONS: You have a choice of slope--from a
vertical of 0° to a slope of 15°.
This is the choice range:

Which is your most comfortable letter slope?
Whichever letter slope you choose, use that
slope for all your writing.

LOOK at your writing.

 Do you have an even letter slope?

Yes___ No___

SLOPE GUIDE:

Make your own slope guide to fit your choice of letter
slope. Place a sheet of notebook paper at an angle under
your writing paper and line up the lines with your letter
slope.

 Do your letters have different slopes?

Yes___ No___

PLAN how to write with an even letter slope.
Use the following exercise to find a
comfortable slope for you.

1. write word

2. draw slope lines
   over letters

3. pick one slope

4. draw parallel lines

5. write over slope lines

Choose a letter slope and write all your
letters using that slope.

Use paper clips or removable tape to hold the two sheets
together. On the undersheet outline the edge of the
writing paper so you know where to place the next sheet
of paper.

| 0° | 5° | 10° | 15° |

SPEED: TIMED WRITING Use the timed writing to help increase speed.
The goal is to increase the number of words written per minute.
Begin by writing the following sentence (or another sentence) as a warm-up.

A quick brown fox jumps over the lazy dog.

1. TIME LENGTH: 1 MINUTE Write the sentence at your most comfortable speed. If you
   finish before the time is up, begin the sentence again. Count the number
   of words written. Write this number in the margin.
2. TIME LENGTH: 1 MINUTE Write the sentence a little faster. Try to add one or two more
   words to your total. Count the number of words written.
3. TIME LENGTH: 1 MINUTE Write the sentence as fast as you can. Count the number of
   words written.
4. TIME LENGTH: 1 MINUTE Write the sentence at a comfortable speed. Count the number
   of words written. Write the number in the margin.

Repeat process
once a month.

 Compare the total of #4 to #1.
Did you increase the number of words written by one or more? Yes___ No___

EYES CLOSED   Using the same sentence, do this exercise as a follow-up to the
timed writing. Use a non-lined sheet of paper. Close your eyes. Picture in your mind's eye
the shape of each letter as you write. Take all the time you need.
You may be amazed how well you can write with your eyes closed.

6mm lines

© 2010 Getty-Dubay
Getty-Dubay Italic Handwriting Series
available from Allport Editions: **www.allport.com**

5mm lines

© 2010 Getty-Dubay
Getty-Dubay Italic Handwriting Series
available from Allport Editions: **www.allport.com**

5mm lines with capital height

© 2010 Getty-Dubay
Getty-Dubay Italic Handwriting Series
available from Allport Editions: **www.allport.com**